FUN WITH PHONICS

Learn to read with

Jen the hen

Words by Sue Graves
Illustrations by Jan Smith

book-studio

Ben had a hen called Jen the hen.

Ben had ten hens. Jen was hen number ten.

One day Jen got out of her pen.

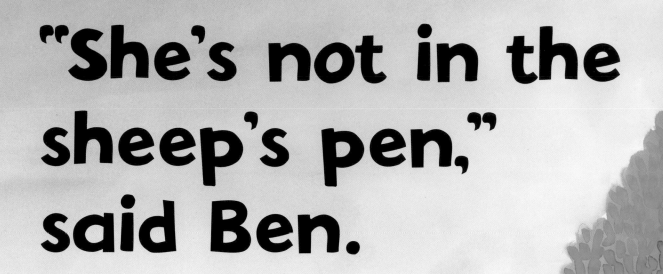

"She's not in the sheep's pen," said Ben.

"And she's not in my den."

"She might be in the pig pen," said the men. "We'll soon find Jen."

There in the pig pen was Jen with Len.

"There she is!"

"Come on Jen," said Ben. "Back to your pen, then."

"Sorry Jen."

The end